Adventures of Saint Paul

*A*dventures *of* *S*aint *P*aul

By Oldřich Selucký

Translated by
Marianne Lorraine Trouvé, FSP

Adapted by
Christina Miriam Wegendt, FSP

Illustrated by Zdeňka Krejčová

*P*auline
BOOKS & MEDIA
Boston

Library of Congress Cataloging-in-Publication Data

Selucký, Oldřich, 1955-
  [Pavel, dobrodruh viry. English]
  Adventures of Saint Paul / by Oldřich Selucký ; translated
by Marianne Lorraine Trouvé ; adapted by Christina Miriam
Wegendt ; illustrated by Zdeňka Krejčová.
     p. cm.
  ISBN 0-0190-0786-9 (pbk.)
  1. Paul, the Apostle, Saint Juvenile literature ? Apostles—
Biography—Juvenile literature. I. Wegendt, Christina Miriam,
1979- II. Krejčová, Zdeňka. III. Title.
  BS2506.5.S3913 2008
  225.9'2–dc22

                              2008012243

"P" and PAULINE are registered trademarks of the Daughters of St. Paul.

Copyright © 2004, Karmelitánské nakladatelstvi s.r.o. Kostelní Vydří
Czech Republic , www.kna.cz

Published by Pauline Books & Media, 50 Saint Pauls Avenue, Boston,
MA 02130-3491.

Printed in the U.S.A.

ATSP KSEUSAHUDNHA03-1039176 0786-9

www.pauline.org

Pauline Books & Media is the publishing house of the Daughters of St.
Paul, an international congregation of women religious serving the
Church with the communications media.

2 3 4 5 6 7 8 9   14 13 12 11 10

Contents

1
The Tentmaker's Son

"Saul, have you finished your chores?" the tentmaker asked. He walked into the workroom, but it was empty.

"Not again!" he groaned. "Where's that boy gone now? I'll bet I know."

Leaving his unfinished tent behind, the man stepped out into the bright sunshine. He headed for the synagogue in their town of Tarsus. This was the Jewish house of prayer. It was also the place where boys studied the Jewish faith.

Saul's father wasn't surprised to find his son inside. Saul was asking his teacher, the rabbi, lots of questions.

"There you are, Saul!"

Saul turned around and saw his father. The boy became very quiet.

"Didn't we talk about this already, son? First do your chores. Then you are free to bother the rabbi with your questions."

"I'm sorry, Father," Saul replied. "It's all just so interesting!"

The rabbi laughed. "Oh, it's no problem. But it sounds as if you'd better head home, Saul."

The rabbi turned to Saul's father.

"Saul is a smart young man," he said. "He loves our Jewish faith very much. I think he's ready to go to school in Jerusalem."

"At the school of Gamaliel, the famous rabbi?"

"Yes," replied the rabbi. "Saul has many gifts. One day we may hear great things about him."

Gamaliel was one of the greatest Jewish teachers alive. Saul could hardly believe his luck! He was able to travel to Jerusalem and study there for many years. When he finished school, Saul, too, became a rabbi.

At around this time, the teaching of someone called Jesus began to spread. Jesus' followers said he had risen from the dead. They said he was the Son of God. Soon other people began to believe in Jesus, too.

Saul didn't agree. He thought the followers of Jesus were wrong. They were confusing people. Saul knew that something had to be done!

2
Saul Meets Jesus

"Look out! The soldiers are coming!"

Saul of Tarsus was leading a search for all the Christians in Jerusalem. He wanted to arrest them so they couldn't talk about Jesus anymore.

As the soldiers marched down
the street, a Christian carpenter
named Jacob stood still. He real-
ized his children were still playing
outside.

Their mother ran out.

"Come inside quickly, children!"

The family waited in the house,
hoping the soldiers wouldn't stop.

The heavy stomping of the soldiers'
boots drew near. Suddenly someone began pounding on the front
door. Bam, bam, BAM!

"Open up!" shouted the leader of
the soldiers. Suddenly the door flew
open. Saul and a soldier walked in.

"You are under arrest for being
followers of Jesus of Nazareth," said
Saul. He pointed at the mother and

father. "Take them to prison!" Then he turned and left.

Later that evening, Saul went to the home of his old teacher, Gamaliel. He still loved to ask questions. But tonight something was bothering Saul.

"Peace be with you, Saul," Gamaliel said as he welcomed Saul into his home.

"Gamaliel, what do you think about the followers of Jesus of Nazareth?" Saul was nervous as he waited to hear what his teacher would have to say.

"I think that if the teachings of Jesus are false, this excitement won't last long. His followers will disappear. But if his teachings

come from God, no one will be able
to stop the truth from spreading.
That's my opinion. Wait—and you
will see."

"Oh. I see. Well, thank you,
Gamaliel," Saul replied respectfully.
This was not the answer Saul wanted. He wanted to take action, not sit
and wait!

The next day Saul made up his mind. If he waited, it might be too late. People everywhere would begin hearing about Jesus. He decided to travel to the town of Damascus. Many followers of Jesus lived there. Saul wanted to arrest them. He would end this nonsense once and for all!

The trip from Jerusalem to Damascus was long and tiring. The sun beat down on Saul and on the soldiers with him. Some of the soldiers complained. But not Saul! He was on a mission.

Suddenly, from the clear blue sky, a bright light shone down on Saul. It was so bright that Saul couldn't see anything. He fell to the ground and heard a voice.

"Saul, why are you persecuting me?"

The soldiers ran to help Saul, but he didn't budge. They had no idea what was going on.

"Who are you, sir?" Saul asked the strange voice.

Very gently, the voice replied, "I am Jesus."

In that moment, something changed in Saul's heart. Suddenly he understood. *Now I know why all my threats could not stop people from believing in Jesus*, he thought. Gamaliel had been right.

To the relief of the soldiers, Saul finally got up. The light had been so bright that he couldn't see anything. The soldiers had to lead him by the

hand into the city.

Saul stayed in Damascus for three days. He still couldn't see. On the third day, a man named Ananias came to visit Saul.

"Saul, Jesus has sent me here," Ananias said. "He sent me so you may see again and be filled with the Holy Spirit."

Suddenly Saul was able to see the man standing before him!

"Ananias, now I understand. Please, I want to be baptized," Saul said.

Ananias baptized him then and there. Saul wanted to begin telling others the Good News right away. Jesus really had risen from the dead! He really was the Son of God!

But the other followers of Jesus were afraid. Maybe this was a trick.

"How could Saul have changed his mind like that?" asked one.

"Perhaps he's still planning to arrest us," said another.

"It would be better not to trust him," agreed a third.

Saul left Damascus and went to Arabia. But one day he would return to teach people about Jesus.

3

An Amazing Escape

Saul finally returned to Damascus and began preaching. Many people still didn't trust him. Others didn't believe in Jesus' teachings at all. They were angry that he had become a follower of Jesus. These people decided to kill Saul!

But Saul had made some friends among the Christians. They heard about these plans and warned him.

"We have a plan for you to escape, Saul," they told him.

That night Saul met his friends by the city wall. They were carrying a long rope and a huge basket. *What could their plan be?* Saul wondered.

"Don't be afraid, Saul. This rope is very strong. Climb into the basket, and we'll lower you over the wall of the city. When you reach the bottom, you'll be safe from your enemies."

Saul was nervous. He got into the basket. *I trust that God will be with me*, he thought.

It seemed to take forever for the basket to bump the ground. When it finally did, Saul jumped out. He took one look back. Then he waved goodbye to his friends—and ran as fast as he could! He was headed back to Tarsus.

Saul wondered what he should do next. He went to Jerusalem to meet the apostles. One of the Christians, named Barnabas, became his good friend.

Together they went to Antioch. From there, they started on a long trip to tell people about Jesus. Saul started using his Roman name, Paul.

Paul and Barnabas had many adventures. Once, on the island of Cyprus, Sergius Paulus, the Roman leader, asked them to visit him. He wanted to hear about Jesus. One of his friends was a man who pretended to be a prophet, a person who speaks for God. This man was known as Elymas the magician.

Elymas was angry that Sergius was interested in Jesus. *What kind of nonsense are these two going to tell*

him? he thought. *I'll spy on them and find out.*

When Paul and Barnabas arrived, Elymas hid behind a curtain. He listened to everything they said. The more Elymas heard, the angrier he felt. These two were going to take his position as advisor to Sergius. How dare they!

The magician jumped out from behind the curtain.

"Do not listen to these men, Sergius Paulus!

They tell you lies. I'm the only one you can trust!" Elymas's eyes were blazing. As he spoke, he stamped his feet.

Paul stepped forward and spoke.

"Elymas, you don't really care whether we are speaking the truth or not. You only want to make sure you keep your important position. Because you can't see your own selfishness, you will now lose your sight for a short time. Maybe then you'll see that some things are worth more than power."

As Paul spoke these words, everything became dark as night for Elymas the magician. He was very afraid. But someone came and kindly led him from the room.

Sergius Paulus watched in amazement. Surely these Christians were speaking the truth.

"Paul, Barnabas, can you baptize me right away?" he asked.

Just as Paul said, Elymas the magician was soon able to see again. But he probably didn't pretend to be a prophet anymore!

4
Two Close Calls

Barnabas and Paul continued their travels. One day they were walking along a river. Suddenly Barnabas shouted to Paul.

"Look out!"

Just then an arrow flew over Paul's head.

"Bandits! They're behind the rocks. What will we do?" Barnabas exclaimed.

"They must think we have lots of money," said Paul. "Let's throw this sack to them. Then we can cross the river before they catch us."

Barnabas threw the sack to the bandits. Then the two friends ran as fast as they could.

The bandits couldn't believe how easy this was. They grabbed the sack and tore it open.

"Argh! They've left us their lunch. Capture them!" cried the robbers.

But Paul and Barnabas were already safely on the other side of the river.

Their next stop was the city of Lystra. The people who lived there prayed to many gods. Paul began to speak to a crowd gathered nearby.

"There is only one God! He made the whole world."

Nearby a man sat by the road, begging. He had never been able to walk. Paul stretched out his hand to him.

"Get up, my friend."

The man looked up at Paul. Then he jumped up off the ground. After so many years, he could finally walk. It was a miracle!

The crowd began to cheer.

"These visitors must be gods!" someone shouted.

The noise grew louder. A band started to play. People began trying to give gifts to Paul and Barnabas.

"Stop, my friends!" Paul shouted. "We're people just like you. It was God who healed this man. It wasn't us!"

The music stopped. The crowd was confused. Then someone at the back of the crowd began to shout.

"I know these two! They are dangerous men. The one called Paul

escaped from Damascus. Be careful. He'll bring trouble to Lystra!"

"We don't want trouble in Lystra. Go away!" shouted the mob.

The crowd chased Paul and Barnabas out of the city. Some people even picked up stones. They began to throw them at Paul. Barnabas tried to help his friend, but he was pushed out of the way. Some of the stones hit Paul. He fell to the ground.

"That will teach them not to cause trouble in Lystra!" someone yelled.

When most of the crowd had gone home, Barnabas rushed over to Paul.

"Are you all right?" he asked.

Paul opened his eyes and looked around. Three people were walking toward them.

"We're Christians," said one. "Can we help?"

The three put Paul on a small cart and took him to their home. Soon he felt better. In no time, Paul was ready for his next adventures for Jesus.

5
The Earthquake

"Where next, Paul?" asked Timothy, one of the Christians from Lystra.

Barnabas had decided to go and preach in Cyprus. Now Timothy was traveling with Paul. A man named Silas and a doctor called Luke were with them too. Luke took notes about their adventures. He wrote them in a book that's part of the Bible. We call this book the Acts of the Apostles.

"I'm not sure, Timothy," Paul said.

That night Paul didn't sleep very well. He had a dream that a man from Macedonia begged them to come and talk about Jesus. The next morning Paul was very excited.

"We're off to Macedonia!" he said.

After they arrived, Paul and his friends went to pray near a river. They found a group of women praying too. Paul and the others joined them. Afterward Paul began to

tell them all
about Jesus.
One woman
listened very
carefully.
Her name was
Lydia. She sold
purple cloth
and was very
rich.

"I believe
that what
you're saying
is true, Paul. Jesus *is* our Savior. He
died to save us from sin. Would you
baptize me?" she asked.

Paul baptized Lydia, and the
four travelers stayed at her house.
Soon after, they went into the city

of Philippi...where trouble
was waiting for them!

One day Paul, Timothy,
Silas, and Luke were walking in the city. They talked
about Jesus with people
they met. Soon they saw a
woman who was a slave.
An evil spirit gave her the power to
know things about the future. The
man who kept her as a slave made
lots of money through her fortune-
telling. When the woman saw Paul,

she began to follow him, shouting wildly, "These men are servants of God!"

Everywhere Paul and Silas went, the woman followed them. She kept yelling the same thing. She was out of control! Finally Paul began to feel annoyed. He turned around and spoke to her.

"My daughter, your power to know the future wasn't given to you by our loving Father.

It comes from the devil. The devil doesn't want us to trust in God. God wants to free you from this evil spirit," said Paul. "He wants you to live in peace."

The woman stopped shouting and became very calm. She looked at Paul and began to smile.

"Thank you, Paul. I've been so unhappy," she said. She gave Paul a big hug.

Suddenly her owner appeared. He was very angry! Paul had wrecked his plans to make money.

"Guards!" he shouted. "Take these men away from here. They are destroying my business!"

Two soldiers took Paul and Silas away. They were brought before a judge. The judge sent them to jail.

Paul and Silas were in their cell that night, praying and singing. Suddenly something strange happened. The jail began to shake. It rocked up and down. Then it rocked from side to side. There was a big RUMBLE!

"It's an earthquake!" cried Paul.

The jail shook so hard that all the doors swung open. The prisoners' chains came loose. They were free!

The jailer woke up. He saw the open doors and felt afraid. If all the prisoners escaped, he would be in really big trouble. What would he do?

But Paul and Silas hadn't run away. "We're still here," Paul told the guard. "You're not in trouble."

The jailer was confused. Why did they stay? Did Paul and Silas really care what would happen to him if the prisoners escaped? This was amazing!

"Paul, you must tell me all about Jesus. I want to be his follower too," the guard said.

That night, Paul baptized the jailer and his whole family. The next day, the judge released Paul and Silas.

6
The Unknown God of Athens

The city of Athens was famous
for its great temples and monu-
ments to the Greek gods. When Paul
arrived, he noticed a simple monument standing alone. On it were
written the words, "To an Unknown
God." Paul was curious.

"What does this mean?" he asked a man walking down the street. "Who is the unknown god?"

The man smiled.

"Well, we pray to so many gods. Someone was afraid we may have missed one. So they built this monument, just in case we left someone out."

The next day Paul went to a place where the citizens of Athens discussed new ideas. Many people were sitting and talking. He began to tell them about Jesus.

"People of Athens! I'm here to tell you about the God who has been unknown to you. He is the only God, the Creator of the world. We are all his children. God has sent his

Son, Jesus, to us. Jesus was raised from the dead!"

Some of the people in the crowd began to laugh. They had heard many new and unusual ideas before. But this was the strangest idea of all. No one could be raised from the dead!

"Very funny, Paul. Tell us another story," someone said.

Paul was upset. His trip to Athens wasn't turning out as he had hoped. They were making fun of him.

These people didn't really want to hear about Jesus. Paul wouldn't be able to share the Good News with them. Sadly he walked away. One man ran after him.

"I'm sorry the others were so rude to you. My friends and I would like to know more about Jesus. Would you tell us?" he asked.

"Of course I'll come with you. I'll tell you everything you want to know," Paul said, smiling. He was very happy. Maybe his trip to Athens wouldn't be so bad after all!

7
Trouble in Ephesus

After his visit to the great city of Athens, Paul stayed for a long time in another city in Greece. It was called Corinth. He made friends there with Christians who were tentmakers, just as Paul was.

One night Jesus appeared to Paul in a dream. Jesus encouraged Paul to be brave. He promised to always take care of Paul, no matter what.

Later, Paul sailed back to Antioch. On the way he passed through a city called Ephesus. A few months later, he returned to Ephesus to preach.

"Watch out! Did you hear? Paul of Tarsus is coming to Ephesus," called a man, sticking his head out

a window. "He causes trouble wher-
ever he goes."

"I hear he teaches that we should
love each other and worship only
one God," said an old woman, lean-
ing on her cane. "I'm not sure what
to make of that."

"What, no idols?" asked a young
man. He was holding a scroll. "I
don't think he'll like Ephesus very

much. We have lots of silversmiths here, artists who make idols out of silver. Many other people study witchcraft. No one in Ephesus will listen to Paul."

But Paul loved it in Ephesus. Every day he taught more and more people about Jesus. He told them how much God loves us and wants to forgive us when we do something wrong. He explained that Jesus was the Son of God who rose from the dead.

Many people believed what Paul taught them. They stopped buying the silversmiths' idols. Finally a lot of Paul's new friends got together. They threw their books of witch-craft and evil spells into a big bon-fire.

When Demetrius the silversmith heard about this, he was worried. He saw people throwing their books of evil spells into the big fire. He knew they would no longer worship the idols he made. How would he make money? Paul was going to ruin everything! He had to be stopped.

So Demetrius gathered all the silversmiths together. They marched into the town square. They shouted, "The gods of Ephesus are very great!" They didn't want people to begin worshiping the one God that Paul was preaching about.

The silversmiths shouted so loud and so long that the leaders of the town came to see what was wrong. Soon they discovered that the crowd was angry with Paul. They

tried to convince everyone to go home. Paul hadn't broken the law. The leaders didn't want anyone to get hurt.

Paul wanted to talk with the silversmiths, but it was too dangerous. The men were still too upset. Paul's friends were afraid he would get hurt. Finally Paul left the city of Ephesus. Later he wrote a letter to the followers of Jesus who lived there. He sent his friend Timothy to lead the Church in that city.

Paul decided to return to Jerusalem. His friends warned him that he had many enemies there. But Paul wasn't afraid! He remembered that Jesus was always with him.

8
Shipwreck!

"Didn't I tell you he'd return?"
whispered the man with the long
grey beard. He frowned, "It's him.
Over there!"

The other two men peeked out
from behind the stone pillar. They

were just in time to spot Paul and one of his Greek friends walking by the Temple. They thought Paul was bringing his friend into the Temple. This was very wrong, they thought. Only people who followed the Law of Moses could pray in that holy place. They ran after Paul.

"Attention, everyone," yelled the man with the grey beard. "Paul of

Tarsus has returned. He doesn't respect our Temple anymore. He teaches people strange things. This must stop!"

The crowd began to shout at Paul. Some people tried to attack him. They dragged him away. Thankfully there was a Roman soldier nearby. He saw what was happening to Paul and rushed over to help.

"What do you think you're doing?" he asked.

"Take this man away! He's breaking the law!" someone cried out.

The soldier arrested Paul and led him away quickly.

But Paul still wasn't safe in Jerusalem. The soldiers took him to another city, where the Roman governor lived.

After Paul had been a prisoner for almost four years, he asked to go to Rome. He thought the emperor might set him free.

Soon Paul was put onto a ship with some other prisoners. His friend Luke was with him. Together they would make the long and difficult voyage to Rome.

The ship had been at sea for many days. "I've sailed these waters before," Paul said to his guard. "We'd better find a good, safe place to spend the winter. It's dangerous to make the rest of the journey until the weather is good again."

The guard agreed. "I'll ask the captain what his plans are."

The captain of the ship was a fat little man who had spent many

years at sea. He was moving huge
sacks of grain. They were almost as
big as he was! The guard went up to
him.

"Captain, are we planning to
spend the winter somewhere safe
from bad weather?"

"Jumping jellyfish!" the captain
exclaimed. "Are you joking? If we
wait that long, all this good grain

will be spoiled. I'll only be paid if I deliver it safe and sound. We must keep going!"

The guard returned and told Paul what the captain had said. Paul was worried, but he trusted in God.

A good, strong breeze pushed the ship along in the right direction. The captain was very pleased with himself.

"Why, slimy sea monsters!" he said happily. "I made a good decision! After all, I'm the captain!"

One of the sailors climbed up to look out at the horizon. He could see a very small cloud forming far away. It grew bigger and bigger as they sailed toward it. Soon the sky grew very dark.

"A storm is coming," he warned the other sailors. Soon everyone was busy tying things down and preparing for a rough ride. The captain looked around helplessly. Rain began to pour from the dark clouds. The wind blew hard. Lightning lit up the sky.

"Sweet suffering swordfish!" he exclaimed. "Bring down the sails!"

The storm continued all night long. Everyone was afraid. Finally the captain gave the order to begin throwing the grain overboard. If they didn't, the ship would surely sink.

For two whole weeks the storm continued. The ship's crew, the guards, and the prisoners were all very hungry.

"Leaping lobsters!" cried the captain. "If only we could be rescued!" But how could they be rescued now?

Paul tried to encourage the others. "God will take care of us," he told them.

"Land! I see land ahead!" yelled one of the sailors.

The rain had stopped, and the sky was brighter. The crew tried to sail the ship in the direction of the island. But the waves were huge. The ship hit a giant rock and began to sink! Everyone jumped overboard and swam for shore.

9
Paul's Last Adventure

The prisoners, guards, and crew all reached the island safely. They were wet and tired and miserable. Then they noticed something. They weren't alone. The people of the island had seen the shipwreck.

Already they were building a nice, warm fire. Paul helped to gather wood.

"Welcome to the island of Malta," a man named Publius said. "We thank God that you are safe."

Paul dropped some dry branches on the fire. Suddenly he felt a stab of pain in his hand. *What was that?* he thought.

"It's a snake!" cried Publius.
"That's the most deadly type of
snake on Malta. There's no cure for
its bite. You'll surely die."

Everyone watched Paul. They
were very worried. No one could
survive the bite of that snake. Luke,
the doctor, was with Paul. He was
sad because he had no medicine to
cure his friend.

Everyone waited. Paul would surely die soon. But nothing happened. Paul was fine. This was certainly a miracle! Everyone was amazed.

Publius invited Paul and his guard to stay at his home until they could continue their journey. Publius' father was very sick. Paul prayed for him, and he became well

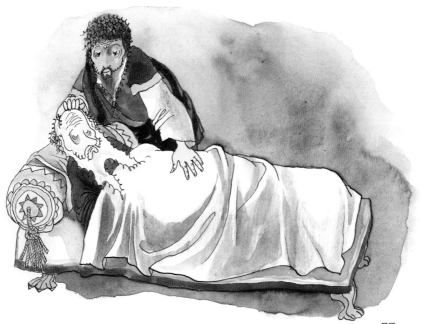

again. News of this spread all over Malta. Many sick people asked Paul to pray for them. They were cured too.

Paul and the others stayed there many weeks. Finally it was time to leave.

"Thank you for your kindness, Publius," Paul said. Many of the people on the island came to say goodbye to Paul. They would miss him. A few people even began to cry. There was no way to know if they would ever see him again.

Paul and Luke, the soldiers and the sailors set sail again for Rome. This was to be Paul's final adventure.

When they arrived, Paul was kept under arrest, but he still told people about Jesus. He wrote letters to the people of the churches he had visited over the years.

After two years, Paul went before the emperor. But the emperor wouldn't listen. Many Christians were being arrested and even killed for believing in Jesus. The emperor sentenced Paul to death.

Paul remembered the day he had met Jesus on the road to Damascus. *Ever since then, I've wanted everyone else to have the chance to know Jesus, too,* he thought. *I've been very lucky!*

Paul died bravely for his faith. In all his adventures, he had shown great love for God. Paul preached to

thousands, wrote many letters, and traveled all over the known world. He helped many people to understand how much God loves us. We still admire Paul as one of the greatest saints of all.

How Do I Say That Word?

Antioch—AN-tee-ock

Athens—ATH-inz

Damascus—duh-MAS-kus

disciple—di-SY-puhl

Ephesus—EF-uh-sus

Jerusalem—jeh-ROO-sah-lem

Lystra—LIS-truh

Macedonia—mas-i-DOH-nee-uh

monument—MON-yoo-ment

persecute—PUR-si-kyoot

Philippi—FIL-uh-pie

prophet—PROF-it

rabbi—RAB-eye

savior—SAYV-yer

synagogue—SIN-uh-gog

How Do I Say That Name?

Ananias—an-uh-NY-uhs

Barnabas—BAR-nuh-bus

Demetrius—di-MEE-tree-us

Elymas—EL-ih-mus

Gamaliel—guh-MAY-lee-uhl

Lydia—LID-ee-uh

Publius—POOB-lee-us

Sergius Paulus—
    SUR-jee-us PAWL-us

Silas—SY-lus

Prayer to Saint Paul

Saint Paul,
　You had so many adventures as you followed Jesus. No matter what happened, you always trusted that God was with you. Help me to love and trust God as you did. Help me to share God's love with my family, my friends, and everyone I meet.
　Amen.

Saint Paul
COMIColor Saints

By Virginia Helen Richards, FSP, and D. Thomas Halpin, FSP

Kids will love this comic-book-style coloring and activity book. Action-packed pages include some of the most exciting adventures of Saint Paul. Activity pages and cut-out trading cards add hours of extra fun! Ideal for children ages 6–8.

Booklet   32pp.

#71095 $2.95 ($3.75 Cdn)

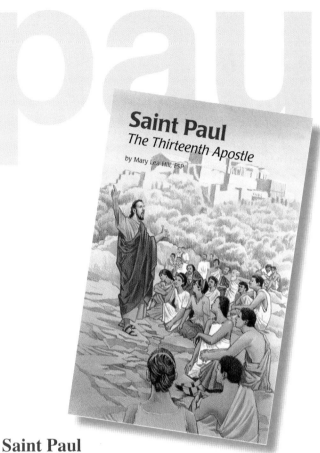

Saint Paul
The Thirteenth Apostle
By Mary Lea Hill, FSP

From a persecutor of the early Christians, St. Paul was changed forever when he met Christ on the way to Damascus. Although he was not one of the original twelve apostles, he became known as the "thirteenth apostle." He traveled great distances, preaching and writing as he went along, to bring the Gospel of Jesus to everyone. His great love for the Lord and for all people will inspire young readers to follow his example! Perfect for children ages 9–12.

Paperback   128pp.
#71028 $7.95 ($9.95 Cdn)

Who are the Daughters of St. Paul?

We are Catholic sisters. Our mission is to be like Saint Paul and tell everyone about Jesus! There are so many ways for people to communicate with each other. We want to use all of them so everyone will know how much God loves us. We do this by printing books (you're holding one!), making radio shows, singing, helping people at our bookstores, using the Internet, and in many other ways.

Visit our Web site at www.pauline.org

BOOKS & MEDIA

The Daughters of St. Paul operate book and media centers at the following addresses. Visit, call or write the one nearest you today, or find us on the World Wide Web, www. pauline.org

CALIFORNIA
3908 Sepulveda Blvd, Culver City, CA 90230   310-397-8676
2640 Broadway Street, Redwood City, CA 94063   650-369-4230
5945 Balboa Avenue, San Diego, CA 92111   858-565-9181

FLORIDA
145 S.W. 107th Avenue, Miami, FL 33174   305-559-6715

HAWAII
1143 Bishop Street, Honolulu, HI 96813   808-521-2731
Neighbor Islands call: 866-521-2731

ILLINOIS
172 North Michigan Avenue, Chicago, IL 60601   312-346-4228

LOUISIANA
4403 Veterans Memorial Blvd, Metairie, LA 70006   504-887-7631

MASSACHUSETTS
885 Providence Hwy, Dedham, MA 02026   781-326-5385

MISSOURI
9804 Watson Road, St. Louis, MO 63126   314-965-3512

NEW YORK
64 West 38th Street, New York, NY 10018   212-754-1110

PENNSYLVANIA
9171-A Roosevelt Blvd, Philadelphia, PA 19114   215-676-9494

SOUTH CAROLINA
243 King Street, Charleston, SC 29401   843-577-0175

VIRGINIA
1025 King Street, Alexandria, VA 22314   703-549-3806

CANADA
3022 Dufferin Street, Toronto, ON M6B 3T5   416-781-9131